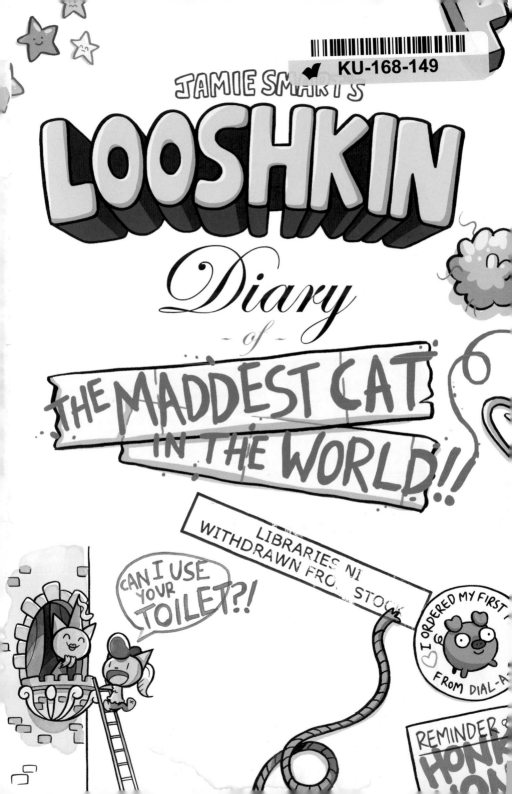

JAMIE SMART'S

LOOSHKIN

Diary

~ of ~

THE MADDEST CAT IN THE WORLD!!

CAN I USE YOUR TOILET?!

I ORDERED MY FIRST
FROM DIAL-A

REMINDER
HON

I NEED A CAT!

DING DING!

I JUST SOLD THEM ALL, I'M AFRAID.

ALTHOUGH, THERE IS ONE I COULDN'T SELL...

ARE YOU SURE YOU WANT 'IM?

STORE

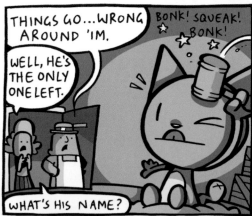

THINGS GO...WRONG AROUND 'IM.

WELL, HE'S THE ONLY ONE LEFT.

WHAT'S HIS NAME?

BONK! SQUEAK! BONK!

BUM!

BOSH!

LOOSHKIN

AND SO BEGINS OUR TALE OF...

...THE MADDEST CAT IN THE WORLD.

FART!

FFRP!

6

IN THE BACK GARDEN...

LADY LOOSHKIN OF LOOSHIRE, IT IS MOST WONDERFUL OF YOU TO JOIN OUR **GARDEN TEA PARTY**.

I EVEN BAKED A **CAKE**, TO CELEBRATE!

OH NO, I FORGOT THE CLOUDY LEMONADE! WHAT A BAD HOST YOU MUST THINK ME.

WAIT THERE! I'LL BE RIGHT BACK!

MEANWHILE, INSIDE LOOSHKIN'S MIND...

SCREEE-EEAM!!

HELP US! SHE'S QUITE MAD!

8

Today I will... COLOUR IN WITH LOOSHKIN!

Colour in this PIG!!

oinkle!

Colour in this AEROPLANE!!

brmm!

Colour in my FACE!

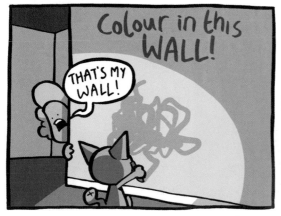

Colour in this WALL!

THAT'S MY WALL!

COLOUR IN GRANDPA!!

WAIT! STOP!

AH, GREAT (RICH) AUNTIE FRANK! I'M SO GLAD YOU COULD COME AROUND FOR A MORNING COFFEE!

HMPH!

I **HEAR** YOU HAVE RECENTLY PURCHASED A **CAT.**

WELL...

WELL, NOTHING. YOU KEEP IT AWAY FROM US.

MY PRIZE WINNING POODLE **PRINCESS TRIXIBELL** HAS A VERY DELICATE CONSTITUTION.

THE SLIGHTEST FRIGHT, AND HER FUR BEGINS TO FALL OUT!

SHAKY SHAKE!

UH. OH...

NO NEED TO WORRY, GREAT AUNT. I HAVE SHUT LOOSHKIN IN WITH THE CHILDREN UPSTAIRS.

HMPH.

THERE WILL BE **NO** FRIGHTS.

UPSTAIRS...

BWOOARGHH!

SCREAMM!

EDWIN, WHY CAN'T WE WATCH _MY_ TV SHOWS? WHY DO WE ALWAYS HAVE TO WATCH Y__O__UR HORRID FILMS?

MY ROOM. MY TV.

WELL, I DON'T LIKE IT. KEEP ME SAFE, MISTER BEAR.

BWOARGH!! SCREAM!

LOOSHKIN! THAT IS **NOT** FUNNY!

MIAOW?

ALL OF YOU, PIPE DOWN! MY FAVOURITE EVER MOVIE IS ON!

THIS ONE'LL MAKE YOU **WET YOURSELVES.**

IT CAME FROM THE **ATTIC!**

27

DON'T FORGET! LOOSHKIN'S BIRTHDAY

HAPPY BIRTHDAY, ME!!

HAPPY BIRTHDAY, ME! AUGH! GET OUT!

SHOOF!

IS THIS A TRICK? IS THAT 'CAKE' JUST A BALLOON COVERED IN ICING, READY TO **EXPLODE?**

HE THINKS IT'S **HIS** BIRTHDAY.

BUT LOOSHKIN, WE DON'T KNOW YOUR BIRTHDAY. WE DON'T KNOW WHEN YOU WERE **BORN**.

INSIDE LOOSHKIN'S HEAD...

DID WE BLOW UP ALL THESE BALLOONS FOR NOTHING?

NO. IT'S PROBABLY OUR BIRTHDAY.

WE. WILL. PARTY!

HANG ON, HOW DID WE GET OUT HERE?

BACK HOME...

WELL DONE, EVERYONE. PRETENDING WE'D FORGOTTEN LOOSHKIN'S BIRTHDAY SO WE COULD SET UP THIS SURPRISE **PARTY!**

AND HE LEFT HIS CAKE BEHIND, TOO!

NOW WE JUST WAIT FOR HIM TO SHOW UP...

HONK! HONK!

THE SHED
GO FOR IT!
HEY.
HEY, CAT.
HEY, YOU. CAT.
YOU'RE A STUPID CAT.
I'M MISTER BUNS, AND I DON'T LIKE OTHER CATS BEING IN MY NEIGHBOURHOOD, Y'HEAR? SO YOU'D BETTER JUST...
HEY.
WHAT'S YOUR NAME, ANYWAY?
ARE YOU EVEN LISTENING TO ME? HEY! WHAT'S SO INTERESTING ABOUT THAT SHED, ANYWAY?
EARLIER...
LOOSHKIN, UNDER NO CIRCUMSTANCES ARE YOU TO GO IN MY SHED!
SERIOUSLY, AREN'T YOU SCARED OF ME? I'M THREATENING YOU!

MEANWHILE...

SIGH.

ANOTHER DAY OF EATING BISCUITS AND BROWSING THE INTERNET.

OH! WHAT'S THIS?

VIDEO

TRENDING

STUPID CAT BEING STUPID

5 MILLION VIEWS

LOL AMAZING
OMG DID HE DIE?

BUY GUM CREAM

CAT-LADY DATING

HA HA HA! HOW SWEET! WHAT A FUNNY CAT THAT IS, HE DESERVES TO BE A STAR!

HANG ON!

IT'S THE CAT NEXT DOOR!

SANDRA

TELLY AWARD WINNER!

THIS IS MY CHANCE!

DING DONG!

HELLO, I'M YOUR NEIGHBOUR, **SANDRA ROTUND.** I USED TO PRESENT MY OWN DAYTIME TV SHOW, BUT MY CAREER ENDED AFTER I ATE TOO MANY SWEETS AND TRIED TO SHAVE MY STUDIO AUDIENCE.

I'VE BEEN WAITING ALL THIS TIME IN MY DRESSING GOWN UNTIL I COULD RETURN TO TV - AND YOUR **CAT** IS MY TICKET TO MID-MORNING STARDOM!

GLEE!

THEY'LL LET ME BACK ON TV IF I CAN GET A LOOSHKIN EXCLUSIVE!

THAT CAT IS VERY SPECIAL.

I HEAR THAT A LOT.

SO... WELCOME BACK TO **SANDRA**, MY BRAND NEW TV SHOW, STARRING YOUR HOST... **ME!**

AND WE'RE ABOUT TO MEET A REAL INTERNET CELEBRITY!

MEET **LOOSHKIN**, THE LATEST INTERNET CAT SENSATION. FOOTAGE OF HIM FIRING A TEDDY BEAR INTO A SHED HAS ALREADY GONE VIRAL WITH OVER 16 BILLION VIEWS.

LOOSHKIN, HOW DOES IT FEEL TO BE SHOT INTO THE LIMELIGHT?

MIAOW?

HAHAHA! HOW CUTE!

WELL, AS OUR GUEST OF HONOUR, WE THOUGHT PERHAPS YOU'D LIKE TO HELP OUT ON THE COOKERY SECTION OF OUR SHOW.

WHAT? NO.

WE DON'T LET HIM NEAR CUTLERY.

WE DON'T LET...

45

WHAT?

OH LOOK, MISTER BUNS! FOOTAGE OF YOU BEING RUN OVER BY A POTATO-POWERED TRACTOR HAS HAD **WAY** MORE VIEWS THAN THE LOOSHKIN VIDEO!

NEWS! NEW INTERNET CAT!

NEWS! NEW INTERNET CAT!

AT LEAST **ONE** OF US IS ON TV.

ALAN JOHNSON!

LOOSHKIN WAIT!! WHY ARE YOU CHASING ME WITH A FRYING PAN?

HUH?

YOU? I'VE BEEN CHASING **THIS FLY!**

OH.

IT'S GONE.

WELL, OKAY THEN. NO HARM DONE. LET'S JUST GET BACK TO NORMAL, EH?

A FEW MINUTES LATER...

EGGY BUBBLES!

HOW MANY FLIES CAN THERE **BE?**

LOOSHKIN, YOU HAVE ANGERED A **LOT** OF CLOWNS.

WHICH ARE CLOWNS?

ARE THEY THE ONES WITH **WIBBLY UDDERS?**

WIBBLY UDDERS WBBLBBB!

NO, THAT'S COWS.

OH, **PHEW!**

WHY ARE YOU HOLDING A JAM JAR?

UMMMMM. I'VE FORGOTTEN.

IS IT TO KEEP **YOU** IN?

ARGH!! GERROFF!

PLOMP!

BZZ!

WAIT! NO! IT WAS TO CATCH A **BEE!**

GETTOUT.

SHAKE! SHAKE!

OOF!

BEEEEEEEE!!!

GIBBER!

YOU'RE CATCHING A BEE TO LET IT OUT?

THAT'S UNUSUALLY HELPFUL OF YOU.

STUPID BEAR. I'M GOING TO MAKE IT BITE ME SO I GET **BEE POWERS!!!**

BUZZ! BUZZ! BUZZ!

NOW THEY'LL LET ME IN THE CIRCUS!

WAGGLE!

WHAT A STUPID BEAR.

SMASH! GRUHH!

HONKK!

THE CLOWNS! THEY FOUND US!

SAVE YOURSELF! EEE!

DONK!

?

IT'S NOT WORKING, MASTER! THEIR DEFENCES ARE TOO STRONG!

VERY WELL. ZEN PERHAPS IT IS TIME...

...WE **UNLEASH TINY ZE CLOWN!**

'TINY'? PFFT, HE SOUNDS LIKE A PUSHOVER.

BEES!

THEY FART HONEY OR SOMETHING!

HE'S COMING THIS WAY! AND HE'S **BRINGING** THE LASER WITH HIM!

IF I GET BITTEN BY A RADIOACTIVE LASER BEAM, MAYBE I'LL TURN INTO A **SUPERHERO.**

TURN IT OFF! TURN IT OFF!!

I WAS ONLY EATING **BROCCOLI!!**

THIS IS FOR YOU, YOU MEAN, **MEAN CAT!!**

I'M READY! I'M **READY!**

AWW, LOOK AT LOOSHKIN TWITCHING IN HIS SLEEP.

I BET HE'S DREAMING ABOUT CHASING MICE OR SOMETHING.

HEY THERE, KIDS! AH'M... **CAP'N FRUITCAKES!** AND AH'M PROTECTING MAH **TREASURE CHEST,** FILLED WITH **DELICIOUS, BRIGHTLY COLOURED CEREAL!**

L...AH, THERE YOU ARE. DO STOP STARING AT THAT CEREAL, WE HAVE A VERY IMPORTANT VISITOR!

THIS IS **PROFESSOR FRUMPLES,** THE WORLD'S LEADING EXPERT ON **CAT PSYCHOLOGY.**

WE'VE HIRED HIM TO **ASSESS** YOU.

INSIDE LOOSHKIN'S BRAIN...

IT'S HIM!

IT'S CAP'N FRUIT-CAKES!

AND HE'S BROUGHT HIS TREASURE!

CHOMP! CHOMP!

NO, LOOSHKIN! DON'T EAT HIS BRIEFCASE!

LET HIM BE, MRS JOHNSON.

IT IS ESSENTIAL WE GIVE ZIS CAT WHATEVER HE WANTS, IN ORDER TO DISCOVER HIS TRUE DESIRES.

SO TELL ME, KITTY CAT. WHAT IS IT YOU REALLY, REALLY WANT?

IS IT A BOWL OF MAH DELICIOUS, MULTI-COLOURED, CEREAL?

SCORE!

71

I DECLARE YOU TO BE AN ENEMY OF FROGTOPIA!

ALL HAIL FROG-BURT!

GO FOR IT!

I'M NOT TO BLAME.

WHAT A LOVELY DAY IT IS OUTSIDE! JUST THE RIGHT WEATHER TO STAY IN BED AND READ COMICS.

YOU SHOULD BE **OUTSIDE!** GARDENING!!

WHAT'S THIS? IS THIS A GAME?

JUST DO WHAT THE FROG SAYS.

AW, LOOSHKIN. YOU'RE PLAYING WITH A PUPPET?

THAT'S SWEET.

NOT ONLY A PUPPET! HRRRGHHHHH!!

HRGHHHHH!

BRUM!

MAYBE LOOSHKIN'S STRUGGLING TO EXPRESS HIS EMOTIONS?

WELL, I'M CERTAINLY NOT STRUGGLING TO EXPRESS MINE.

THIS HAS GONE FAR ENOUGH.

YOU ARE BEING A VERY NAUGHTY CAT. GIVE ME THAT PUPPET!

SNATCH!

HE DOES THINGS. THINGS WITH **BALLOONS.**

DID... DID HE JUST TIE A BUNDLE OF BALLOONS TO MY ANKLE?

NO, MISTER FROGBURT! NO!

YES!

RUN, LOOSHKIN!

WHERE TO, MISTER FROGBURT?

SOMEWHERE HOT AND LEAFY!

ZOO!

POISON FROG ENCLOSURE

DEY DON'T RESPECT ME HERE! YOU'RE ON YOUR OWN!

MISTER FROGBURT? MISTER FROGBURT?

THE SPARROW

GO FOR IT! 👍

TODAY IS OFFICIAL **PIG DAY**

OINK!

BE SURE TO TAKE A PIG INTO SCHOOL, WORK OR ON THE BUS!

THE BLUETIT

SO THERE I WAS, CARRYING ALL MY SAVINGS, WHEN THE WIND BLEW EVERYTHING UP IN THE AIR.

I WOULD HAVE LOST ALLLL MY MONEY, IF IT WEREN'T FOR...

OUR LOCAL SUPERHERO!

SUPERHERO INDEED. I BET HIS NAME'S GARY, AND HE WORKS IN THE SUPERMARKET.

AND HE PICKED IT ALL UP FOR YOU?

OH, YES. NOW ALL THE MONEY I HAVE IS CRAMMED IN THESE CARRIER BAGS!

HOPE NOTHING ELSE HAPPENS TO ME!

WHAT A NON-NEWS STORY, WASN'T IT LOOSHKIN...

LOOSHKIN?

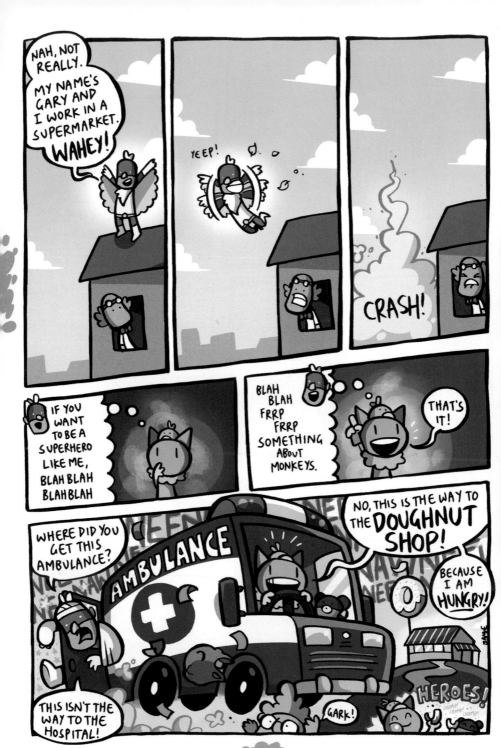

DON'T FORGET! BEAR'S BIRTHDAY

YYYYYYYOINK!

LOOSHKIN? WHAT ARE YOU DOING?

IT'S **BEAR'S BIRTHDAY** TODAY! WE MUST **CELEBRATE!**

IT IS?

WE MUST?

CLOMP! CLOMP!

COME AND SEE!

HEY! WHAT ARE YOU DOING IN MY ROOM?

NOT YOUR ROOM!

Bear bbday srpiz

BEAR'S BIRTHDAY SURPRISE!

HELP ME.

MISTER JOHNSON WOULD LIKE TO TELL YOU A STORY:

HUB GLUB GLUBBY GLUB!

THAT'S A RUBBISH STORY!

SHOPPING LIST:

DOG CHEESE!

LOOSHKIN, WHERE HAVE YOU BEEN? YOU'RE COVERED IN LEAVES!

NEVER MIND, THERE'S NO TIME TO WASTE! YOU HAVE TO PUT ON YOUR HELMET, AND TAKE YOUR SWORD!

CLONK!

FOR YOU ARE THE BRAVE KNIGHT, SIR LOOSHALOT, AND YOU HAVE COME TO RESCUE ME...

...THE BEAUTIFUL PRINCESS...

STOMP! STOMP! STOMP! STOMP!

...FROM THE TOP OF THE TOWER!

LOOSHKIN, WHY ARE YOU WEARING A BUCKET?

YOU KNOW WHAT, IT DOESN'T MATTER. JUST AS LONG AS YOU STAY OUT OF THE WAY THIS EVENING, YEAH?

GREAT AUNTIE FRANK IS VISITING.

SO TO KEEP HER HAPPY, I'M SERVING SOME OF THE WORLD'S FINEST **CHEESES!**

GOAT'S CHEESE! BUFFALO MOZZARELLA! SHEEP'S MILK CAMEMBERT!

PONG!

ANYWAY, **YOU** CAN'T HAVE THEM. SO STAY AWAY!

AND TAKE THAT BUCKET OFF YOUR HEAD, YOU LOOK RIDICULOUS.

INSIDE LOOSHKIN'S MIND...

ANIMALS! CHEESE!

ANIMAL CHEESE?

CALL THE PROFESSOR!

YOINK!

HOW DOES THE CHEESE COME OUT?

NOPE. NO IDEA.

DO DOGS HAVE POCKETS?

LOOK IN ITS POCKETS!

JUST DO SOMETHING!

CHEESE

SQUEEZE!

THE SOUND OF A BAG OF NEW POTATOES BEING EMPTIED ONTO THE CARPET.

I DON'T THINK THAT'S CHEESE.

IT SMELLS LIKE CHEESE THAT DIED!

THPTH-BTHHH!

GO FOR IT! 👍

THIS WEEK FILMED IN GLORIOUS RASPBERRY -O- VISION!

THPTHBTHHH

HEY, LOOK AT LOOSHKIN! HE'S BEING FUNNY!

THPTHBTHHH

WHAT IS IT, BOY? ARE YOU PRETENDING TO RIDE A MOTOR BIKE?

HA HA! WHAT A SILLY CAT!

★SLAM!★

LET'S DRAW LOOSHKIN

Then cross it out

moo

and draw a PIG instead!

DON'T FORGET! PLUMBER

BRRR! IT SURE IS COLD IN THIS HOUSE TODAY!

HANG ON, WHO SET THE THERMOSTAT TO MINUS 90 DEGREES?

DINGDONG!

A PLUMBER!

YOU LOOK A LOT LIKE OUR CAT.

W...WHERE ARE YOU GOING? WE DON'T NEED A PLUMBER IT'S THE THER—

PLUMBER!

EEE HEE HEE!

A WEIRD MAN IS AT THE DOOR.

EAT YOUR GREENS

KNOCK KNOCKITY KNOCK KNOCK!

AH, HELLO, OLD LADY, MY NAME IS **TERRY PICKLES**, MP, AND I WAS WONDERING IF I COULD COUNT ON YOUR VOTE IN THE NEXT ELECTION?

GOODNESS, ARE YOU ALL RIGHT?

I'M AN OLD LADY!

I KNOW, BUT...UH...

WHAT NOISE DO OLD LADIES MAKE?

OH, YES.

BAROOOO

COME WITH ME, YOUNG MAN! YOU'RE JUST IN TIME!

IN TIME? IN TIME FOR WHAT?

...THE SÉANCE!

OBBBBBBBVIOUSLY.

DUH!

I, UH, I NEED TO GO HOME NOW. I'M SUDDENLY FEELING A LITTLE BIT GASSY.

THE SPIRITS!

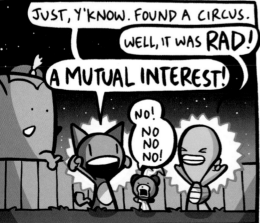

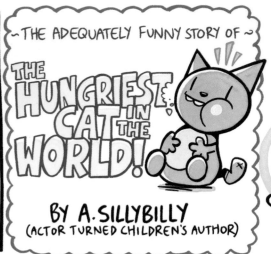

~ THE ADEQUATELY FUNNY STORY OF ~

THE HUNGRIEST CAT IN THE WORLD!

BY A. SILLYBILLY
(ACTOR TURNED CHILDREN'S AUTHOR)

This episode:

ONCE UPON A TIME, THERE WAS A BLUE CAT.

ONE DAY THE BLUE CAT WOKE UP, AND HE WAS HUNGRY.

RUMBLE RUMBLE BUMBLE BOO

SO, HE ATE SOME CEREAL.

BUM FLAKES

AND THEN HE ATE A PORK CHOP.

AND THEN HE ATE A WHOLE BUNCH OF BANANAS.

AND THEN HE ATE SOME SPAGHETTTTTTI BOLOGNAYYYYS.

DID HE MAKE THAT HIMSELF?

AND THEN HE ATE A CAKE SHAPED LIKE A BOTTOM.

HIS OWNERS TOLD HIM TO STOP EATING AND GO OUTSIDE.

SHOO!

BUT THE BLUE CAT WAS STILL HUNGRY.

THE SOUND OF STEEL DRUMS!

SO, HE ATE A **TYRE**.

THEN A **BICYCLE**.

THEN A **SHED**.

HOI!

THEN A **HUGE LORRY**.

JOBBIES

AND THE **MORE** HE ATE, THE **BIGGER** HE BECAME.

SOON HE WAS SO BIG, HE COULD EAT THE **MOON.**

AND THEN HE NOTICED THE **EARTH...**

AND IT LOOKED **DELICIOUS.**

YOU'RE A **BAD CAT!**

DING DONG!

AH, HULLO, LITTLE GIRL. SORRY I'M LATE.

L.... LITTLE GIRL?

IT IS ME, **OTTO VON BOTTO**, THE WORLD'S GREATEST **GHOST HUNTER!**

YOU CALLED ME HERE TO RESOLVE ALL YOUR PROBLEMS!

MY DICKY TUMMY?

YOUR **GHOST!** I SHALL FIND IT, AND EXPEL IT!!

FRRP!

WITH THESE SPECIAL **NIGHT VISION GOGGLES,** I WILL BE ABLE TO SEE ANY **PARANORMAL ACTIVITY.**

WOULD YOU LIKE A FISH FINGER?

HWOOOOOARGHH!!

Y...**YOU!** WHERE DID YOU GET THAT FISH FINGER?

I FOUND IT IN THE BIN!

LOOK, MISTER BOTTO, I ASSURE YOU WE NEVER CALLED FOR A GH...

TO THE BIN!

FINALLY!

AND WITH MY **HEAT DETECTING CAMERA,** I'LL BE ABLE TO SEE IT.

GASP! THE ENTITY... IT'S...IT'S... **BEHIND YOU!**

POOOOO YEAH, I CAN SMELL IT TOO.

I ATE A LOT OF CABBAGE, OKAY?

HE DIDN'T FIND YOU AT **ALL.**

I'LL CALL ANOTHER ONE.

DUE TO A NUMBER OF INCIDENTS, INCLUDING A RAMPAGING CLOWN, A STEAM TRAIN, DANCING ELEPHANTS, PORTALS TO HELL AND **FREQUENT** TOILET EXPLOSIONS, YOUR HOUSE IS NOW STRUCTURALLY UNSOUND.

BUT...I'M AN **INVENTOR!** A **CRAFTSMAN!** EVERY TIME SOMETHING SMASHES THROUGH A WALL, I PATCH IT BACK UP AGAIN!

WELL, IT'S NOT ENOUGH. I'LL NEED TO CONDUCT A SURVEY.

GRR, THIS IS ALL **LOOSHKIN'S** FAULT!

WHERE IS HE ANYWAY?

TAP TAP TAP!

YOU ARE THE MOST BEAUTIFUL

CAT I HAVE EVERRRR SEEN!

THANK YOU MISTER BUNS, THAT IS VERY NICE OF YOU TO SAY.

LOOSHKIN, CAN YOU DO ANY BETTER?

HA HA! WELL, I DO LIKE A BOYFRIEND WHO CAN MAKE ME LAUGH.

THBTH

AND YOU BROUGHT ME SUCH A THOUGHTFUL GIFT, TOO.

UM.

WHATEVER IT IS.

WHAT IS IT?

I DUNNO. FOUND IT.

I BELIEVE IT IS A **TREBUCHET.** MORE COMMONLY CALLED A CATAPULT.

HIS SILLY INVENTOR OWNER PROBABLY BUILT IT. WHICH MEANS IT'S **VERY** UNLIKELY THAT IT ACTUALLY W...

TWANG!!

NYAAAA!

WELL, MISTER JOHNSON, AFTER AN EXTENSIVE SURVEY, I CONCLUDE YOUR HOUSE **IS** JUST ABOUT SAFE TO LIVE IN.

HOORAY!

NYAHHHHHHH

PLINK!

CRUMM MMBLE!

THPTHBTHHH.

THPTH.

I CAN'T HELP BUT FEEL THAT SOMEHOW THIS WAS LOOSHKIN'S PLAN FROM THE VERY START.

THPTHBTHH

DON'T BE SILLY, DEAR.

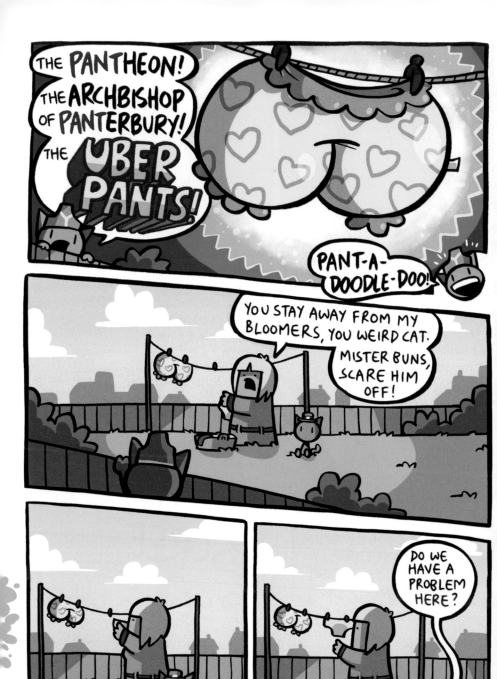

NOW NOW, DON'T BE SO HASTY, MAN. THE AGREEMENT WAS FOR US TO REACH THE FABLED CITY OF **SHANGRI-LA** INSIDE A HOT AIR BALLOON -AND WE ARE NOT THERE YET.

OH, BUT WE MUST BE **CLOSE**, JOHNSON. WE ARE SO HIGH AMONGST THE CLOUDS!

IN FACT, PASS ME THE MAGNIFYING SPECTACLES. I...I THINK I SEE SOMETHING.

LOOSHKIN, WHAT DO YOU HAVE IN THAT JAR? IS IT BEES AGAIN?

IS IT **BEES**?

IS IT **BEES**?

LOOSHKIN, IS IT **BEES**?

IT'S MIIIINE!

IS IT BEES THO.

BEEE EEEEES!

YOU PUT THEM OUTSIDE. RIGHT NOW!

GOODNESS, JOHNSON! THE HIGHER WE GO, THE WORSE THE TURBULENCE.

HOLD ONT THE SIDES

SHAKESHAKE

OH, WAIT. IT STOPPED.

AUGH! THE SPECTRE IN THE CLOUDS! IT IS UPON US AGAIN!

HOLD FAST, I'LL GET MY RIFLE.

BLOW HIS FLIPPIN' NOSE OFF!

BONUS COMICK
WHAT'S DIS? COMICSES?
I am Looshkin.
I MIGHT BE SICK.
He is Bear. We are friends.
EUGH!
We... what?
I like to HUG!!
I MIGHT BE SICKER.
You're squeezing me too hard!
YES.
YOU PUTS DEM IN YOUR COMIC HOLE.
I had so much potential!
NGGGG!
YOU SHOULD READ A MISTER FROGBURT COMIC
POP!
OKAY YES THANK YOUS.

SHOPPING LIST:
1. WEAPONS-GRADE PLUTONIUM
2. CHIPS

NATIONAL **PIG DAY!**

IT'S ON ITS WAY!

PIGS!

ACTIVITIES!

MORE PIGS!

NATIONAL PIG DAY IS ANNOUNCED THE DAY AFTER IT HAS HAPPENED.

SHOPPING LIST

A LOVELY TIME

HEY, NO FAIR! THIS BOX OF **MARSHMALLOW CRUNCH** IS **ALL** CRUNCH!

HAHA- YOU LOSE! I GOT **ALL** THE MARSHMALLOW, CONGEALED INTO...

DONK!

SHAKE! SHAKE!

THE SWEETEST, MOST SUGARY BALL OF SUGAR IN THE UNIVERSE!

AHHHHHHH

LOOSHKIN! NO LIVING THING CAN EAT THAT MUCH SUGAR IN ONE GO!

HOMP!!

SHOULD WE CALL A VET?

CHOMP CHOMP

WE ARE ALL MADE OF STARDUST.

WE ARE ALL MADE OF STARS.

FOUND HIM!

YOU MEAN HE'S BEEN OUT IN THE WOODS ALL THIS TIME?

WHAT WAS HE DOING?

NOTHING.

HE JUST DOES ...NOTHING.

I DON'T LIKE IT.

LOOSHKIN'S USUALLY SCREAMING, OR HITTING THINGS.

HE'S NEVER **THIS** QUIET.

WHAT DO WE **DO**?

PLINK! PLUNK! PLINKY PLINKPLUNK!

PLINY PLINK PLUNK!

LEAVE HIM ALONE, REGINALD. HE'S CLEARLY A SIMPLETON.

HEE HEE!

LISTEN, CAT-NOBODY-WANTED, YOU'RE AN EMBARRASSMENT TO THE NAME OF CAT.

THE RUNT OF OUR LITTER.

OF POOR BREEDING.

WE, HOWEVER, ARE PROPER CATS. ELEGANT, WELL-GROOMED.

BRUSH! BRUSH!

DIGNIFIED, AND GRACEFUL.

HOP! HOP!

ONCE I MADE A WATER-SLIDE BUT I COULDN'T FIND ANY WATER SO I USED CHUTNEY!

SIGH...

GO BACK INSIDE YOUR HOUSE, AND ACT MORE LIKE A CAT.

OKAY! BRMMM!

CATS DON'T BRMM!

WE'RE YOUR BROTHERS AND SISTERS! **PROPER CATS!** DON'T YOU REMEMBER? WE'VE BEEN TALKING TO YOU FOR THE LAST **TEN MINUTES!**

SHRUG!

ONE MORE CHANCE. GO AND HUNT THAT BIRD, AND BRING IT TO YOUR HUMAN OWNERS AS A GIFT.

LIKE A **CAT** WOULD DO.

AND **NO** TRICKS. NO CHEESE, NO CARS, NO SILLY NOISES!

JUST A **CAT.**

HUNTING A **BIRD.**

THAT'S GOOD!

GOOD!

SHUFFLE! SHUFFLE!

BWOOZT!

HALLOO BIRRDYY!

BRUM! BRUM! BRUM!

HOW ARE YOU FEELING TODAY?

BABY!

I'M HAVING A BABY!!

LOOSHKIN, WHAT'S THAT STUFFED UNDER YOUR DRESS?

MEHHHH BEHHBEHHH!

BUT THAT'S... IMPOSSIBLE!

YOU'RE A... BOY CAT.

FRPP! FRRP!

THIS MUST BE SOME KIND OF MIRACLE!

BWOOOARGHH!

PFFT! IT'S NO MIRACLE. I SAW LOOSHKIN EATING A WHOLE JAR OF PICKLES IN HIS SLEEP. THAT'S WHY HIS TUMMY IS SO BIG.

CRAVINGS! FOR MEHH BEHBEHH!

LIMESCALE! FROM THE KETTLE!! MMMM! CRAVINGS! BEHBEH!

CRUN CRUNC CRU CRUNG

(DON'T EAT LIMESCALE! LOOSHKIN IS A TRAINED IDIOT!)

HMM, THAT IS AN ODD THING TO DO...

OUTTA MY WAY! I HAVE TO LIVESTREAM THIS!

LOOSHKIN! YOU'RE THE FIRST BOY CAT TO EVER GIVE BIRTH! HOW DO YOU FEEL?

URF! URF!

BEHHHHH BEHHH

FRRP!

BRRP!

LIVE

TWENTY MILLION VIEWERS ALREADY! PREGNANT LOOSHKIN HAS BECOME A VIRAL SENSATION!

RIGHT! WE NEED TO CONSULT A MEDICAL EXPERT.

THP BTH

PRPPPP!

HURGHHHHH!

I JUST NEEDED TO DO A BIG STAR FART ALL ALONG!

WHEEE!

ALL OUR VIEWERS HAVE GONE!

WHATTTT'S HAPPPENNINGG?!

SHOPPING LIST: DANGER ✰ SAUSAGE ✰

DANGER SAUSAGE!

THIS IS RIDICULOUS, LOOSHKIN! YOU'RE JUST THROWING A SAUSAGE AT DISASTROUS SITUATIONS!

BLOP!

HELP ME! I'VE FALLEN INTO A RAVINE!

JAMIE SMART HAS BEEN CREATING CHILDREN'S COMICS FOR MANY YEARS, WITH POPULAR TITLES INCLUDING *BUNNY VS MONKEY*, *LOOSHKIN* AND *FISH-HEAD STEVE*, WHICH BECAME THE FIRST WORK OF ITS KIND TO BE SHORTLISTED FOR THE ROALD DAHL FUNNY PRIZE.

THE FIRST THREE BOOKS IN HIS *FLEMBER* SERIES OF ILLUSTRATED NOVELS ARE AVAILABLE NOW. HE ALSO WORKS ON MULTIMEDIA PROJECTS LIKE *FIND CHAFFY*.

JAMIE LIVES IN THE SOUTH-EAST OF ENGLAND, WHERE HE SPENDS HIS TIME THINKING UP STORIES AND GETTING LOST ON DOG WALKS.